Best wishes

[illegible] Barclay de Tolly

Published, Illustrated, and Written by - Muriel Barclay de Tolly

Book Design, and Additional Illustrations - Lakuna / Newport, RI

Library of Congress
Copyright office
101 Independence Ave., S.E.
Washington, DC 21559-6000

PRIVATE POST CARD
Haszard & Moore, Importers, Charlottetown, P.E.I.
This Space for Address only.
This Space may be used for Correspondence.
CANADA POSTAGE
ONE CENT
what a beautiful day!
wish you were here.
love,
Puma
Brigitt
Newport, RI
02840
Brigitt
Newport, RI
02840
THIS SIDE IS FOR THE ADDRESS ONLY.

Puma

goes to

The Cliff Walk

of Newport, Rhode Island

by Muriel Barclay de Tolly

Puma had never seen a merry-go-round before. It was so colorful and the waltz-like music made her start to dance. She watched all of the white horses gallop uniformly in a circle, never moving their legs. On the third time around Puma became so excited she leapt up and landed on the saddle of one of the pretty horses. She held on tightly and went round and round, up and down, until she started to feel a little dizzy. When the ride was finished she leapt back down and staggered up the hill.

Still feeling dizzy, she spotted the entrance to the Cliff Walk.

In years past, dances were held on Easton's Beach. Many famous bands played there including Guy Lombardo and Rudy Vallee.

The Merry-go-Round at Easton's Beach

The Entrance to Cliff Walk

The entrance to the Cliff Walk was marked by two large stone pillars which led to a path that seemed to stretch for miles and miles. Puma was both excited and a little nervous about this adventure. She wondered how far the path would take her, and if she would be able to find her way back home?
Then she remembered that this path passed through some of the biggest and most famous backyards in Newport. Finally, Puma reminded herself that she was an adventurous cat and today was to be no exception.

The Cliff Walk is three and one half miles long.
In 1975, the Cliff Walk was designated a National Recreation Trail.

So off

she went

following

the path

On one side of the trail
were big green gardens.....

....and on the other side were crashing waves

at the bottom of a steep steep cliff.

as it twisted

and turned.

Not too far down the path Puma stopped in her tracks. She had noticed a grand opening in the path? It was marked 40 STEPS and led way down to the water below. 40 steps could only mean one thing but Puma needed proof. Down the steps she went counting the whole way....1,2,3,4,5,6,7...until she reached the 40th step. At the water's edge she listened to the waves crash loudly against the rocks. The waves were so big that they sprayed up over the wall and onto her fur. Puma, like most cats, didn't like getting wet, so up she ran, back to the top.

Still a little breathless she continued on her way, and then.....everything went....

In years past, household help from many of the estates gathered at 40 steps on Thursday nights, their one night off, to socialize.

40 Steps

Black!

Had someone turned off the sun?

or was it already nighttime?

Then all of a sudden.....

Everything was light again.

"No need to fear my friend," said a little bird. " It was just a little tunnel some of my army friends built to support this wall from hurricanes. Let me introduce myself. I am Colonel Cardinal and this is my post. I stand guard here every day and night. I haven't taken a day off in 20 years!"

Puma was grateful to the Colonel for calming her down and told him all about her day's adventure.

The Colonel saluted her and wished her luck.

Puma continued on her way...

South of 40 Steps

..and on to a great green lawn where there were many people with books and backpacks moving quickly from place to place. Everyone was sharing ideas and there was a lot of excitement in the air. This must be the University, she thought to herself. Puma had always fancied herself as a cat of great intelligence, and had always dreamed of being the first cat to graduate from college.

Originally, Catherine Lorillard Wolf built Vinland in 1883.
It was renamed Twombley Hall, and is now a part of Salve Regina University.

Twombley Hall

Professor Puma Phd

"That would be the ultimate adventure!" she said.
"'Professor Puma Phd.' That has a great ring to it and I can already see my portrait hanging in the halls of the University."
For now Puma's fantasy would have to wait because she still had a great deal to see on this path. She waved goodbye to the University and promised to return.

" Now this is the life!," Puma said to herself as she lounged on the lawn of the Breakers mansion. This was, by far, the largest mansion she had ever seen. Even the children's playhouse was big enough to live in!

The Breakers is one of the largest mansions on Cliff Walk, and got it's name from the crashing waves that surround its grounds. The house has 70 rooms and 5 floors, and was built in 1885 in an Italian Renaissance style by Cornelius Vanderbilt the second.

The Breakers

Marble House

Further down the path she spotted another grand estate. The Marble House, as it was known, looked like a French Palace. Puma happily strolled around the gardens, took a little nap in the sun, and then ran down toward the water. When she got there she couldn't believe her eyes. Had she walked all the way to China?

The Marble House was built in 1892 and styled after The Petit Trianon at Versailles. The mansion was built by William K. Vanderbilt for his wife Alva's 39th birthday. The interior includes a room decorated almost entirely of solid gold leaf and a dining room made of Alegria Newmidean Red Marble.

"Welcome to the Chinese Tea House " said a little blue bird "Yes, you are still in Newport, Rhode Island. This Tea House was built by the lady of the house. I come here everyday for my afternoon tea. Would you care for some?"

The Chinese Tea House was built in 1914 by Alva Vanderbilt.

Chinese Tea House

Puma sat and sipped her tea as the little blue bird told her all about the history of the Tea House. It was built in 1892 by Alva Vanderbilt, a very wealthy woman. She used the Tea House as a meeting place for the Suffragettes. Suffragettes were a group of women who worked together to bring about a woman's right to vote in 1920. Before that, women were not allowed to vote.

Puma was fascinated by all of the blue birds stories and impressed by his knowledge of the history of Marble House. She was having such a great time with her new friend that she forgot about getting back home.

"Oh my, oh my, I don't mean to be rude," Puma said "but its getting very late and I have to get home. Thank you for your tea and stories. I could listen to them all day, but its time for me to go." So off she ran...

...away from the Tea House..toward the Marble House...past the Breakers...

see you
next time.

....across the University lawn....through the tunnel.....past 40 steps .....and then....

Easton's Beach at the end of the day

...back to Easton's Beach where Puma sat
and watched the sunset before returning
to the home she loved.

photo by William Heydt

Dear Reader,

I hope you enjoyed Puma's adventure on Newport's famous Cliff Walk. It is truly one of the most beautiful spots in the world. If you haven't already done so I invite you to take a day and follow Puma's path.

Love,

Muriel Barclay deTolly

A Special thanks to Peter Martin
of Stacy House for my website,
to Marie Puerini for Proofreading,
to my close Ya Ya friends (Gail, Trish, Brenda, Sue, Carole),
to Ed Morris for his historic knowledge,
Lakuna for designing all my books,

and many thanks for the love and support of my great family:
My Kids - Michael, Paul, Joanne, Wanda, Eric, Katie,
My Grandkids - Erica, Alex, Brigitt, Lela, Ellissa, Caleb, and Sydney -
and last but not least George -
I can never thank you enough.

For more information about my books and cookbooks visit www.murielofnewport.com

Brigitt
Lela
Caleb
PUMA
Puma's Court
Alex
Ellissa
Erica
Sydney

POST CARD

POST CARD

CORRESPONDENCE HERE

the Cliff Walk
was great! See you soon!

love,
Puma

NAME AND ADDRESS HERE

Brigitt
Newport, RI
02840